Ace Academic Publishing
ACHIEVING EXCELLENCE TOGETHER

# SIGHT WORDS

## PART 1 A to N

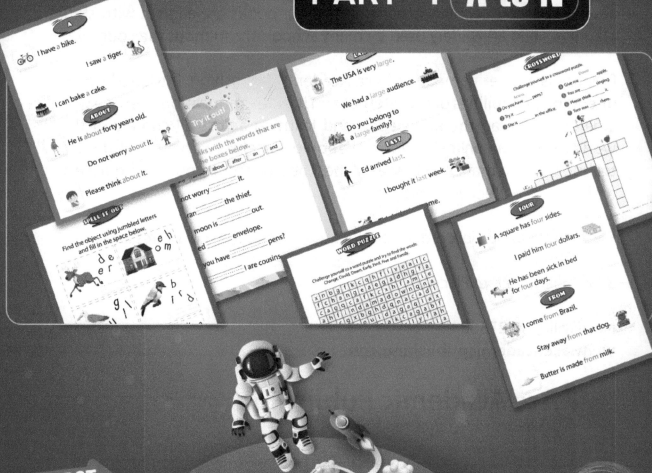

INCLUDES ACTIVITIES & GAMES

www.aceacademicpublishing.com

Author: Ace Academic Publishing

Ace Academic Publishing is a leading supplemental educational workbook publisher for grades K-12. At Ace Academic Publishing, we realize the importance of imparting analytical and critical thinking skills during the early ages of childhood and hence our books include materials that require multiple levels of analysis and encourage the students to think outside the box.

The materials for our books are written by award winning teachers with several years of teaching experience. All our books are aligned with state standards and are widely used by many schools throughout the country.

Prepaze is a sister company of Ace Academic Publishing. Intrigued by the unending possibilities of the internet and its role in education, Prepaze was created to spread the knowledge and learning across all corners of the world through an online platform. We equip ourselves with state-of-the-art technologies so that knowledge reaches the students through the quickest and the most effective channels.

For enquiries and bulk orders, contact us at the following address:

3031 Village Market Place,

Morrisville, NC 27560
**www.aceacademicpublishing.com**

**Ace Academic Publishing**
ACHIEVING EXCELLENCE TOGETHER

ISBN: 978-1-962517-20-1

# PARENT'S GUIDE

Use this book to introduce your child to an exciting new new passion for reading and writing. This book will not only improve your child's communication skills, the colorful puzzles will make learning a fun activity!

**Ace Academic Publishing**
ACHIEVING EXCELLENCE TOGETHER

# Other books from Ace Academic Publishing

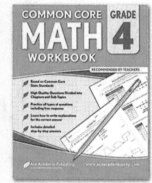

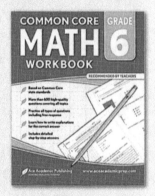
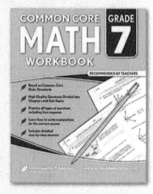

Ace Academic Publishing

ACHIEVING EXCELLENCE TOGETHER

# hello everyone!

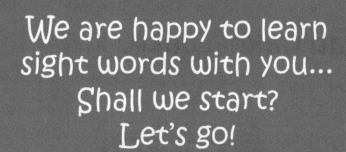

We are happy to learn
sight words with you...
Shall we start?
Let's go!

 I have **a** bike.

I saw **a** tiger.

 I can bake **a** cake.

 He is **about** forty years old.

Do not worry **about** it.

 Please think **about** it.

## AFTER

We ran after the thief.

I went to bed after eating.

After the storm, it was calm.

## AGAIN

Try it again.

Please come again.

It is raining again.

## ALL

All people are equal.

All I have are books.

We all like cycling.

## ALREADY

The moon is already out.

He has already left.

She is already in the office.

## ALSO

I also like cake.

Tom was also there.

He can also speak French.

## ALWAYS

You are always singing.

He is always with me.

We should always obey the law.

**AN**

 I have an idea.

Call an ambulance.

 I need an envelope.

**AND**

 Come and see me.

They can read and write.

 He and I are cousins.

## ANOTHER

I have another sister.

Give me another apple.

I will wait for another 5 minutes.

## ANY

Do you have any pens?

Come at any time you like.

We do not have any sugar.

Try it out!

Fill in the blanks with the words that are provided in the boxes below.

| any | already | about | after | an | and |
|---|---|---|---|---|---|

Do not worry _____ it.

We ran _____ the thief.

The moon is _____ out.

I need _____ envelope.

Do you have _____ pens?

He _____ I are cousins.

**Try it out!**

Write your own sentence based on the sight words given below.

| any | already | about | after | an | and |

_____

- - - - - - - - - - - - - - - - - - -

_____

- - - - - - - - - - - - - - - - - - -

_____

- - - - - - - - - - - - - - - - - - -

_____

- - - - - - - - - - - - - - - - - - -

_____

- - - - - - - - - - - - - - - - - - -

_____

- - - - - - - - - - - - - - - - - - -

_____

# CROSSWORD

Challenge yourself to a crossword puzzle.

**Across**

1 Do you have _____ pens?

2 Try it _____.

3 She is _____ in the office.

**Down**

4 Give me _____ apple.

5 You are _____ singing.

6 Please think _____ it.

7 Tom was _____ there.

ARE

How are you?

You are late.

They are actors.

AROUND

See you around.

He turned around.

I will show you around the city.

## AS

I am as tall as Tom.

Try as hard as you can.

Eat as much as you like.

## AT

Look at me.

I got up at seven.

He works at a bank.

**AWAY**

She looked away.

Put your phones away.

Why did he run away?

**BACK**

He came back soon.

Check back next week.

He drove back home.

## BE

 You will be ok!

Do not be angry.

 I will be watching you.

## BECAUSE

 The bus was late because of the traffic jam.

He cannot come because he is sick.

 I am hungry because I did not eat lunch.

## BEEN

It has been a long time.

Have you ever been on TV?

I have been to the park.

## BEFORE

I have seen her before.

I have never seen a giant panda before.

It began to rain before I got home.

## BEING

I am being patient.

This conversation is being recorded.

I am staying at hotel for the time being.

## BEST

I will do my best.

What flower do you like the best?

I was wearing my best clothes.

# Try it out!

Fill in the blanks with the words that are provided in the boxes below.

| being | away | before | be | been | are |

I will _____ watching you.

Why did he run _____ ?

You _____ late.

It is _____ a long time.

It began to rain _____ I got home.

This conversation is _____ recorded.

# Write your own sentence based on the sight words given below.

| being | away | before | be | been | are |

_____

- - - - - - - - - - - - - - - - - -

_____

- - - - - - - - - - - - - - - - - -

_____

- - - - - - - - - - - - - - - - - -

_____

- - - - - - - - - - - - - - - - - -

_____

- - - - - - - - - - - - - - - - - -

_____

- - - - - - - - - - - - - - - - - -

_____

# Challenge yourself to a picture sudoku.

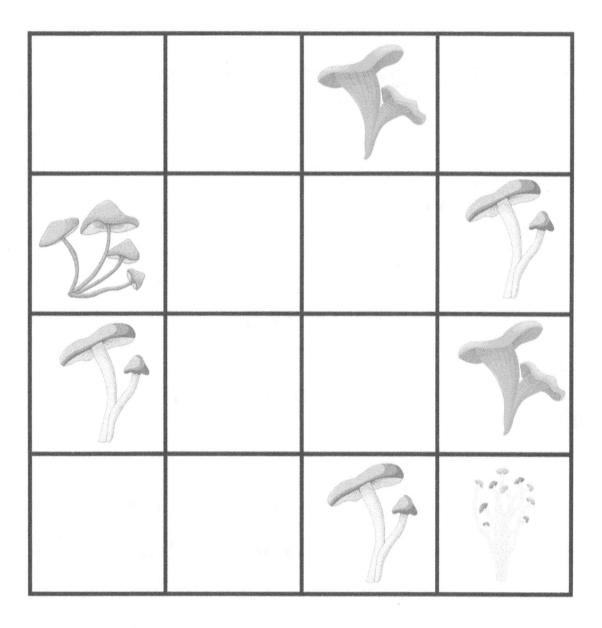

# BETTER

 You will feel better.

It is better to be late than never.

 Tom is getting better.

# BETWEEN

 You must write between the lines.

Please plan to leave between 6 & 7 O'clock.

 I stood between John and Elisa.

**BOTH**

We both agreed upon it.

They both are good teachers.

I can afford one, but not both.

**BUT**

I laughed but it was not funny.

Wood floats, but iron sinks.

I bought a pen, but I lost it.

**BY**

He came by bus.

I need to finish this by tomorrow.

I have to eat by myself.

**CAME**

Mary came to see her dad.

Columbus came in a ship.

Ed came downstairs.

## CAN

I can ski.

Can I open the door?

Mary can swim.

## CHANGE

Keep the change.

Change your clothes.

Did she change her hair?

## COME

Come **in!**

Come **aboard.**

Come **quick!**

## COULD

I could **swim.**

Could **I use your desk?**

He could **speak Spanish and English.**

DID

 Did you miss the shot?

What did she say?

 Did you take a bath?

DO

 I will do it.

Do you recycle?

 I will do my best.

Fill in the blanks with the words that are provided in the boxes below.

| can | do | change | could | by | did |
|-----|-----|--------|-------|-----|-----|

_____ I use your desk?

_____ you recycle?

He came _____ bus.

What _____ she say?

_____ your clothes.

Mary _____ swim.

26

Try it out!

Write your own sentence based on the sight words given below.

| can | do | change | could | by | did |

Challenge yourself to a word puzzle and try to find the words:
About, After, Also, Because, Best, Between & Both.

| q | b | e | t | w | e | e | n | n | a | q | l | x | n | a | s |
|---|---|---|---|---|---|---|---|---|---|---|---|---|---|---|---|
| m | x | l | n | s | a | w | m | a | k | x | a | a | a | k | x |
| a | s | n | a | a | f | t | e | r | a | l | a | l | a | q | a |
| a | k | v | a | n | a | s | q | a | n | x | a | s | a | w | a |
| x | w | a | m | a | x | v | k | a | s | v | a | o | a | m | l |
| v | a | b | o | t | h | a | v | v | m | a | y | s | a | l | a |
| n | s | x | y | s | a | m | s | a | q | k | v | a | c | s | b |
| a | a | b | e | s | t | a | y | a | l | s | o | a | y | a | e |
| a | l | e | q | a | w | a | q | a | l | a | c | x | a | a | t |
| m | a | c | a | v | a | m | a | l | b | x | s | a | a | v | w |
| s | a | a | n | a | q | a | a | b | o | u | t | s | f | a | e |
| x | a | u | a | s | a | w | a | y | x | b | x | a | t | l | e |
| k | a | s | a | k | n | s | b | e | s | t | a | w | e | a | n |
| a | l | e | a | x | a | z | s | h | n | a | b | a | r | a | a |
| m | a | b | o | t | h | w | b | q | a | l | a | k | a | z | m |
| h | q | l | n | a | s | x | a | k | l | a | z | x | b | n | f |

**DOES**

Does he live here?

What does that mean?

Does she play the piano?

**DOWN**

Calm down.

The tree fell down.

Do not let me fall down.

**EACH**

They admire each other.

They each received a present.

They all got one cookie each.

**EARLY**

My teacher let me leave class early.

I eat breakfast early in the morning.

The early bird gets the worm.

**END**

 This road is never going to end.

He went to Paris at the end of May.

 The path leads to a dead-end.

**EVEN**

 Even I cannot believe that.

Two is an even number.

 I will go there even if it rains.

**EVERY**

I go every year.

Tony runs every day.

I shave every morning.

**FACE**

Wash your face.

He has to face his fears.

He lied to my face.

# FACT

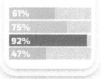

This is based on facts.

I cannot hide the fact from you.

We cannot deny the fact that he is an honest policeman.

---

# FAMILY

Are you close with your family?

I went camping with my family.

The family ate dinner together.

**FAR**

She did not go far.

He walked far away from me.

Is Boston very far from here?

**FEW**

Few people think that I am scary.

She has few friends.

Please buy few oranges.

Fill in the blanks with the words that are provided in the boxes below.

| face | every | few | fell | each | family |

The tree _____ down.

They all got one cookie _____ .

I went camping with my _____ .

He has to _____ his fears.

Please buy _____ oranges.

Tony runs _____ day.

**Try it out!**

Write your own sentence based on the sight words given below.

| face | every | few | fell | each | family |

_____

- - - - - - - - - - - - - - - - - - - - - - - -

_____

- - - - - - - - - - - - - - - - - - - - - - - -

_____

- - - - - - - - - - - - - - - - - - - - - - - -

_____

- - - - - - - - - - - - - - - - - - - - - - - -

_____

- - - - - - - - - - - - - - - - - - - - - - - -

_____

- - - - - - - - - - - - - - - - - - - - - - - -

_____

# Let's learn opposites.

**ASLEEP**

**AWAKE**

**BEHIND**

**IN FRONT**

**BORING**

**INTERESTING**

**AGREE**

**DISAGREE**

**ALONE**

**TOGETHER**

**WHOLE**

**HALF**

## FIND

I have to find it.

I need to find a part-time job.

You can easily find the bank.

## FIVE

She saw five girls outside her house.

Give me five days.

I got up at about five O'clock.

**FOR**

Good for you.

Fry an egg for me.

It will rain for sure.

**FOUND**

I have found it.

We found the chicken alive.

She found him in the kitchen.

# FOUR

A square has four sides.

I paid him four dollars.

He has been sick in bed for four days.

# FROM

I come from Brazil.

Stay away from that dog.

Butter is made from milk.

**Fill in the blanks with the words that are provided in the boxes below.**

| few | four | find | found | for | from |
|-----|------|------|-------|-----|------|

I have to _____ it.

It will rain _____ sure.

I come _____ Brazil.

Give me _____ days.

A square has _____ sides.

She _____ him in the kitchen.

# Try it out!

Write your own sentence based on the sight words given below.

| few | four | find | found | for | from |

_____

_____

_____

_____

_____

_____

_____

# SPELL IT OUT

Find the object using jumbled letters
and fill in the space below.

# WORD PUZZLE

Challenge yourself to a word puzzle and try to find the words:
Change, Could, Down, Early, Find, Five and Family.

| x | n | b | g | f | k | c | q | h | f | i | v | e | a | l | c |
|---|---|---|---|---|---|---|---|---|---|---|---|---|---|---|---|
| f | c | h | a | n | g | e | a | e | g | a | d | h | g | f | a |
| c | a | g | q | c | a | f | k | c | x | h | f | a | m | i | e |
| a | h | f | i | n | d | a | m | a | d | o | w | n | q | n | a |
| f | a | c | g | x | b | g | h | d | q | n | a | c | a | d | l |
| a | a | h | a | c | o | u | l | d | a | g | e | q | l | a | x |
| m | f | i | v | e | a | h | g | a | k | c | a | g | a | b | f |
| i | a | c | h | g | d | a | f | e | a | r | l | y | f | a | h |
| l | n | e | a | r | l | y | a | l | f | e | a | c | q | l | a |
| y | a | a | c | x | g | a | h | g | a | q | h | a | a | k | c |
| a | l | f | a | e | a | g | l | f | i | n | d | k | n | q | o |
| m | f | i | n | d | a | c | a | h | a | m | d | h | y | a | u |
| a | d | a | d | a | g | k | a | c | m | f | l | a | l | f | l |
| f | e | l | o | a | d | a | c | h | a | n | g | e | r | a | d |
| c | a | k | w | a | h | b | a | f | q | e | a | k | a | h | a |
| h | f | a | n | n | a | f | a | m | i | l | y | a | e | b | g |

# GET

 I will get a book from the library.

Will he get well?

 Let us get on the bus.

# GIVE

 Do not give up!

I give you my word.

 Will you give me some money?

**GO**

 Let us go.

May I go home?

 Let us go by car.

**GOOD**

 Good night.

Have a good time.

 This tastes good.

GOT

I got it.

She's got to hurry.

My sister got married.

GREAT

That is a great poem.

He is a great scientist.

The wind feels great today.

**HAD**

We had a good breakfast.

I wish I had a car.

I had a gaming console.

**HAND**

She raised her hand.

The dog bit my hand.

He passed the ball from his hand.

**HAS**

 He has gone out.

She has four cows.

 Spring has come.

**HAVE**

 I have a cat.

Have a nice day.

 Let us have sushi.

**HE**

 He ran.

He is smart.

 He is strong.

**HEAD**

 My head aches.

I should head for a meeting.

 He hit me on the head.

# Fill in the blanks with the words that are provided in the boxes below.

| head | good | has | got | hand | get |

I should _____ for a meeting.

She's _____ to hurry

Let us _____ on the bus.

The dog bit my _____.

Have a _____ good.

He _____ gone out.

**Try it out!**

Write your own sentence based on the sight words given below.

| head | good | has | got | hand | get |

_____

- - - - - - - - - - - - - - - - - - - - - - -

_____

- - - - - - - - - - - - - - - - - - - - - - -

_____

- - - - - - - - - - - - - - - - - - - - - - -

_____

- - - - - - - - - - - - - - - - - - - - - - -

_____

- - - - - - - - - - - - - - - - - - - - - - -

_____

- - - - - - - - - - - - - - - - - - - - - - -

_____

# Challenge yourself to a picture sudoku.

 Can I help you?

Help me, please.

 I will gladly help you.

 I know her.

Give it to her.

 She lost her way.

**HERE**

 I kept my money here.

I eat here.

 Please sit here.

**HIGH**

 She can jump high.

The waves are high.

 I have a high fever.

**HIM**

 I saw him.

She hired him.

 I am waiting for him.

**HIS**

 That car is his.

His eyes are blue.

 He reached his goal.

# HOME

May I go home?

I will stay home.

He felt at home.

# HOUSE

That is our house.

The house is on fire.

A thief broke into the house.

## HOW

How **are you?**

How **tall is Mt. Fuji?**

This is how **I made it.**

## HOWEVER

However, **he is happy.**

However, **there were many** **challenges.**

I like that sweater; however, **it only comes in one color.**

**IF**

Is it okay if I open the can?

He acts as if he is a king.

If I had money, I could buy it.

**IN**

Let me in.

Let's keep in touch!

He arrived just in time.

Fill in the blanks with the words that are provided in the boxes below.

| home | how | her | his | if | here |

_____ eyes are blue.

He acts as _____ he is king.

I kept all my money _____ .

I will stay _____ .

She lost _____ way.

_____ tall is Mt. Fuji?

# Try it out!

Write your own sentence based on the sight words given below.

| home | how | her | his | if | here |
|------|-----|-----|-----|-----|------|

_____
- - - - - - - - - - - - - - - - - - - - -
_____
- - - - - - - - - - - - - - - - - - - - -
_____
- - - - - - - - - - - - - - - - - - - - -
_____
- - - - - - - - - - - - - - - - - - - - -
_____
- - - - - - - - - - - - - - - - - - - - -
_____
- - - - - - - - - - - - - - - - - - - - -
_____

# WORD PUZZLE

Challenge yourself to a word puzzle and try to find the words:
Get, Great, Have, Help, Here, High, House, How and In.

| k | o | h | i | g | h | e | b | g | d | c | l | f | i | b | m |
|---|---|---|---|---|---|---|---|---|---|---|---|---|---|---|---|
| h | a | m | v | f | i | n | c | h | g | g | r | e | a | t | e |
| g | e | t | d | h | h | e | l | p | o | e | k | a | b | i | f |
| o | c | h | e | i | b | f | h | a | v | e | h | g | d | n | m |
| g | h | o | w | h | e | d | h | b | f | l | c | z | i | b | o |
| l | b | h | m | h | a | g | f | h | h | o | w | h | e | r | i |
| h | g | e | t | e | h | e | r | e | w | b | f | h | g | d | g |
| p | b | c | f | i | s | k | g | r | o | m | h | e | e | b | e |
| h | g | h | m | e | a | h | h | i | g | h | w | r | f | i | t |
| i | a | f | i | n | o | c | k | d | e | g | m | e | b | a | h |
| z | e | b | h | d | k | f | n | d | h | e | c | h | h | h | k |
| l | c | g | g | r | e | a | t | h | a | i | f | n | o | o | l |
| b | h | m | d | f | e | h | w | h | g | b | i | h | u | h | i |
| h | o | h | o | u | s | e | k | a | h | b | n | f | s | z | b |
| m | a | l | i | b | g | h | f | v | h | e | a | d | e | w | m |
| e | h | e | l | p | n | d | h | e | a | k | g | i | b | f | a |

It is new.

Who is he?

He is smart.

I got it.

I use it.

It is easy.

## JUST

She just arrived.

We are just watching the televison.

Just do not forget this.

---

## KNOW

I know how to ski.

This is all I know.

I know you can make it.

## LARGE

The USA is very large.

We had a large audience.

Do you belong to a large family?

## LAST

Ed arrived last.

I bought it last week.

This is the last game.

 See you later.

I will call you later today.

 He turned up an hour later.

 She has already left.

Turn left at the corner.

 I am left-handed.

**LESS**

I finished the work in less than an hour.

Dave has less money than John.

You will get there in less than ten minutes.

**LIFE**

Life is fun.

I have life insurance.

I owe him my life.

**LIKE**

I like cats.

Do you like tennis?

We all like cycling.

**LITTLE**

Bob got a little pie.

We had a little water.

I can only speak a little Chinese.

Try it out!

Fill in the blanks with the words that are provided in the boxes below.

| later | last | life | it | if | know |

_____ is easy.

Ed arrived _____.

He turned up an hour _____.

This is all I _____.

I have _____ insurance.

_____ do not forget this.

69

Try it out!

Write your own sentence based on the sight words given below.

| later | last | life | it | if | know |

o r f
g

o
b
t a

i
g d

a
c
t

m
e
r a
h m

a
v r e
g

**LONG**

It is a long story.

How long did you stay?

Ten years is a long time.

**LOOK**

Look at me.

Look behind you.

Do you look your age?

**MADE**

I made Ann a doll.

She made him rich.

He is a self-made man.

**MAKE**

Make it real.

I know you can make it.

Did you make it by yourself?

**MANY**

Many fish died.

Tom has many talents.

Take as many as you want.

**ME**

Let me in.

He took a picture of me with his camera.

Leave it to me.

## MEN

 There are men outside.

I saw two men.

 All men are equal.

## MIGHT

 She might come.

He might not be happy.

 I might be a few minutes late.

# MONEY

 I paid him the money.

Do you have any money?

 He ran away with the money.

# MORE

 I hit the target more than John.

I drank a lot more water.

 We need more workers.

**MOST**

Most people think I am brilliant.

I was in London for most of the summer.

What is his most recent novel called?

**MUCH**

Do not eat too much.

How much is this dress?

I like skateboarding very much.

Fill in the blanks with the words that are provided in the boxes below.

| long | much | money | might | make | more |

Did you _____ it by yourself?

She _____ come.

How _____ did you stay?

He ran away with the _____.

We need _____ workers.

How _____ is this dress?

Try it out!

Write your own sentence based on the sight words given below.

| long | much | money | might | make | more |

_____

- - - - - - - - - - - - - - - - - - - - - - -

_____

_____

- - - - - - - - - - - - - - - - - - - - - - -

_____

_____

- - - - - - - - - - - - - - - - - - - - - - -

_____

_____

- - - - - - - - - - - - - - - - - - - - - - -

_____

_____

- - - - - - - - - - - - - - - - - - - - - - -

_____

# CROSSWORD

Challenge yourself to a crossword puzzle.

| Across | Down |
|---|---|
| **1** Do not _____ up! | **6** This tastes _____. |
| **2** It is a _____ story. | **7** _____, he is happy. |
| **3** She raised her _____. | **8** Do you have any _____? |
| **4** I _____ how to ski. | |
| **5** _____ it real. | |

**MUST**

You **must** go.

I **must** buy one.

She **must** be tired.

**MY**

It is **my** job.

It is **my** treat.

I will do **my** best.

## NEED

 I need **help.**

She needs **your advice.**

 He **didn't** need **proof.**

## NEVER

 Never **tell a lie.**

**It is now or** never.

 **Better late than** never.

## NEXT

 Who is next?

She stood next to me.

 My next door neigbour have a cute little dog.

## NIGHT

 It was dark at night.

How was your night?

 I stayed up all night.

No one was at the game.

There is no hurry.

There is no evidence.

I am not going there.

She may not come.

This is not a problem.

I am leaving now.

It is my turn now.

He is studying now.

I forgot his phone number.

One is an odd number.

Which number bus do you take?

## Try it out!

Fill in the blanks with the words that are provided in the boxes below.

| not | next | now | must | night | no |

I stayed up all _____.

It is my turn _____.

He is _____ in prison.

There is _____ evidence.

Have a _____ good.

Who is _____?

Write your own sentence based on the sight words given below.

| not | next | now | must | night | no |

_____

- - - - - - - - - - - - - - - - - - - -

_____

- - - - - - - - - - - - - - - - - - - -

_____

_____

- - - - - - - - - - - - - - - - - - - -

_____

_____

- - - - - - - - - - - - - - - - - - - -

_____

_____

- - - - - - - - - - - - - - - - - - - -

_____

# Let's learn opposites.

| PULL | PUSH | DOWN | UP |
|------|------|------|-----|

| SAD | HAPPY | CRY | LAUGH |
|-----|-------|-----|-------|

| CLOSED | OPEN | ANICENT | MODERN |
|--------|------|---------|--------|

# SPELL IT OUT

Find the object using jumbled letters
and fill in the space below.

e h n

r a g s s

s i n o c

a n f

f i t g

u b t e r

# Other books from Ace Academic Publishing

   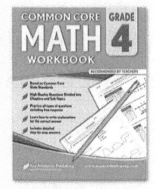

**Ace Academic Publishing**

ACHIEVING EXCELLENCE TOGETHER

# SIGHT WORDS

## PART 1 A to N

ISBN: 978-1-949383-18-8

Ace Academic Publishing
ACHIEVING EXCELLENCE TOGETHER

ww.aceacademicpublishing.com

Printed in the USA
CPSIA information can be obtained
at www.ICGtesting.com
LVHW050324300923
759526LV00009B/1476

9 781962 517201